The
Figure Skating
Training
Journal

The Figure Skating Training Journal: Improve Your
Performance and Achieve Your Dreams. Gold Edition

Achieve Your Dreams Sports Training Series, Volume 2.

Printed in the United States of America

First Printing, 2018

ISBN 978-1-948713-07-8

www.sweetharmonypress.com

Table of Contents

Introduction

Welcome to The Figure Skating Training Journal!

This training notebook, designed by a figure skater, will help you organize your skating goals and practice notes. With these notes you will be able to make better use of your skating and cross-training time, both on and off the ice. You can also use this journal to keep track of your testing accomplishments and your competition experiences.

First, think about the goals you have for the next 3-6 weeks. Read the section "How to set SMART Goals" to learn the best way to think about and make your goals. Write each goal in it's own box in the Goals section of this journal. Share them with your coach and review them weekly to make sure you are doing everything you need to do to make these goals a reality.

Next, use the Skating Practice Notes section during and/or after every lesson with your coach. Take notes on what you practiced, the corrections your coach gave you, and the things you want to remember for the next lesson. Always write down a highlight of the session that you really want to remember or that made you feel great. If you want, give your practice a rating from 1 to 10. This is a fun way to remember really great practice sessions and look back at your progress.

Use the Testing and Competition sections to keep track of the tests you have taken, the competitions you have entered, and the scores and results. This is another great way to track your progress and create lasting records of all your great skating accomplishments.

How to Set a "SMART" Goal

It is important to set goals. It is even more important that these goals be written down and framed in the best way possible to achieve success. The concept of "SMART" goals has been proven to be a winning formula for setting successful goals.

S = **Specific**
M = **Measurable**
A = **Attainable**
R = **Relevant**
T = **Time-limited**

Specific - Make your goal very specific. A goal that says "I want to land an axel someday" is much too vague. Your goal should very clearly define what your success will look like. A better goal would be "I will land a fully-rotate clean axel".

Measurable - You need a way to truly measure your goal. Do you want to say your goal is attained when you have landed the jump once? Or when you have 5 rotations on your camel spin on 3 out of 4 attempts? Find a way to use a number or measurement of some kind to define your goal.

Attainable - Make goals that are attainable in the next few weeks or months. If you want to land an axel one day, but are still working on your waltz jump, then make goals all along the way to achieve the necessary skills to get to your final goal. Make goals for each step in your training.

Relevant - Your goal needs to be a step along to path to your long-term goals. Make sure your goals are worth your time and effort necessary to achieve them. You may want to learn an axel, but if your long-term goal is to be an elite ice dancer, then you might not want to spend the time and effort needed to learn freestyle jumps.

Time-limited - Set a timeframe for your goal. It is important to have a target date to achieve your goal. It is okay if, because of injury, illness, or other reasons you do not achieve the goal in the timeframe you set. But if you don't set a time limit, you may find the goal just drifts off and is forgotten.

The Figure Skating Goal pages give you space to write many goals for your figure skating journey. First, record the date you set the goal and the target date for achieving the goal. In the Figure Skating Goal box, write your very specific goal that you want to achieve. Write exactly what you want to do, and a way to measure how you will know you have achieved this goal.

In the What I Need to Do to Achieve This Goal box, think about the steps you need to take to make this goal a reality. It can be things like "practice 5 days a week for 1 hour a day" or "do 40 sit-up every night to strengthen my core" or "watch training videos to find tips on technique". Use these two areas to write your SMART goal in very specific terms.

When you have met your goal, record the date the goal was accomplished, and notes about what important skills you learned while you were working toward this goal. This is important to reflect on what you learned so that you can apply it to your next set of goals.

Work with your coach or instructor to help define your skating goals. Share your goals with your parents, friends, and skating partners so that everyone is aware of the goals and can be supportive of them. It is great to have someone to remind you of your goals and check in with you on how they are going.

You can have more than one goal at a time. Set multiple goals for the various parts of your skating work is a great way to challenge yourself. Set different goals for jumps, spins, moves in the field, programs, tests, cross-training, and any other parts of your skating. When you accomplish one goal, be sure to set new one, so that you always have something to work on. Remember to review your goals at least once a week, including your past goals that you have completed. It will give you a great feeling of accomplishment to see how far you have come!

Figure Skating Goals

Figure Skating Goals

Date Goal Set	Target Date to Achieve Goal	Date Goal Achieved
Figure Skating Goal	**What I Need to Do to Achieve This Goal**	
What I Learned While Working Toward This Goal		

Date Goal Set	Target Date to Achieve Goal	Date Goal Achieved
Figure Skating Goal	**What I Need to Do to Achieve This Goal**	
What I Learned While Working Toward This Goal		

Date Goal Set	Target Date to Achieve Goal	Date Goal Achieved
Figure Skating Goal	**What I Need to Do to Achieve This Goal**	
What I Learned While Working Toward This Goal		

Figure Skating Goals

Date Goal Set	Target Date to Achieve Goal	Date Goal Achieved
Figure Skating Goal	**What I Need to Do to Achieve This Goal**	
What I Learned While Working Toward This Goal		

Date Goal Set	Target Date to Achieve Goal	Date Goal Achieved
Figure Skating Goal	**What I Need to Do to Achieve This Goal**	
What I Learned While Working Toward This Goal		

Date Goal Set	Target Date to Achieve Goal	Date Goal Achieved
Figure Skating Goal	**What I Need to Do to Achieve This Goal**	
What I Learned While Working Toward This Goal		

Figure Skating Goals

Date Goal Set	Target Date to Achieve Goal	Date Goal Achieved
Figure Skating Goal	What I Need to Do to Achieve This Goal	
What I Learned While Working Toward This Goal		

Date Goal Set	Target Date to Achieve Goal	Date Goal Achieved
Figure Skating Goal	What I Need to Do to Achieve This Goal	
What I Learned While Working Toward This Goal		

Date Goal Set	Target Date to Achieve Goal	Date Goal Achieved
Figure Skating Goal	What I Need to Do to Achieve This Goal	
What I Learned While Working Toward This Goal		

Figure Skating Goals

Date Goal Set	Target Date to Achieve Goal	Date Goal Achieved
Figure Skating Goal	What I Need to Do to Achieve This Goal	
What I Learned While Working Toward This Goal		

Date Goal Set	Target Date to Achieve Goal	Date Goal Achieved
Figure Skating Goal	What I Need to Do to Achieve This Goal	
What I Learned While Working Toward This Goal		

Date Goal Set	Target Date to Achieve Goal	Date Goal Achieved
Figure Skating Goal	What I Need to Do to Achieve This Goal	
What I Learned While Working Toward This Goal		

Figure Skating Goals

Date Goal Set	Target Date to Achieve Goal	Date Goal Achieved
Figure Skating Goal	**What I Need to Do to Achieve This Goal**	
What I Learned While Working Toward This Goal		

Date Goal Set	Target Date to Achieve Goal	Date Goal Achieved
Figure Skating Goal	**What I Need to Do to Achieve This Goal**	
What I Learned While Working Toward This Goal		

Date Goal Set	Target Date to Achieve Goal	Date Goal Achieved
Figure Skating Goal	**What I Need to Do to Achieve This Goal**	
What I Learned While Working Toward This Goal		

Figure Skating Goals

Date Goal Set	Target Date to Achieve Goal	Date Goal Achieved
Figure Skating Goal	**What I Need to Do to Achieve This Goal**	
What I Learned While Working Toward This Goal		

Date Goal Set	Target Date to Achieve Goal	Date Goal Achieved
Figure Skating Goal	**What I Need to Do to Achieve This Goal**	
What I Learned While Working Toward This Goal		

Date Goal Set	Target Date to Achieve Goal	Date Goal Achieved
Figure Skating Goal	**What I Need to Do to Achieve This Goal**	
What I Learned While Working Toward This Goal		

Figure Skating Goals

Date Goal Set	Target Date to Achieve Goal	Date Goal Achieved
Figure Skating Goal	What I Need to Do to Achieve This Goal	
What I Learned While Working Toward This Goal		

Date Goal Set	Target Date to Achieve Goal	Date Goal Achieved
Figure Skating Goal	What I Need to Do to Achieve This Goal	
What I Learned While Working Toward This Goal		

Date Goal Set	Target Date to Achieve Goal	Date Goal Achieved
Figure Skating Goal	What I Need to Do to Achieve This Goal	
What I Learned While Working Toward This Goal		

Figure Skating Goals

Date Goal Set	Target Date to Achieve Goal	Date Goal Achieved
Figure Skating Goal	**What I Need to Do to Achieve This Goal**	
What I Learned While Working Toward This Goal		

Date Goal Set	Target Date to Achieve Goal	Date Goal Achieved
Figure Skating Goal	**What I Need to Do to Achieve This Goal**	
What I Learned While Working Toward This Goal		

Date Goal Set	Target Date to Achieve Goal	Date Goal Achieved
Figure Skating Goal	**What I Need to Do to Achieve This Goal**	
What I Learned While Working Toward This Goal		

Figure Skating Goals

Date Goal Set	Target Date to Achieve Goal	Date Goal Achieved
Figure Skating Goal	**What I Need to Do to Achieve This Goal**	
What I Learned While Working Toward This Goal		

Date Goal Set	Target Date to Achieve Goal	Date Goal Achieved
Figure Skating Goal	**What I Need to Do to Achieve This Goal**	
What I Learned While Working Toward This Goal		

Date Goal Set	Target Date to Achieve Goal	Date Goal Achieved
Figure Skating Goal	**What I Need to Do to Achieve This Goal**	
What I Learned While Working Toward This Goal		

Figure Skating Goals

Date Goal Set	Target Date to Achieve Goal	Date Goal Achieved

Figure Skating Goal	What I Need to Do to Achieve This Goal	

What I Learned While Working Toward This Goal

Date Goal Set	Target Date to Achieve Goal	Date Goal Achieved

Figure Skating Goal	What I Need to Do to Achieve This Goal	

What I Learned While Working Toward This Goal

Date Goal Set	Target Date to Achieve Goal	Date Goal Achieved

Figure Skating Goal	What I Need to Do to Achieve This Goal	

What I Learned While Working Toward This Goal

Figure Skating Goals

Date Goal Set	Target Date to Achieve Goal	Date Goal Achieved
Figure Skating Goal	**What I Need to Do to Achieve This Goal**	
What I Learned While Working Toward This Goal		

Date Goal Set	Target Date to Achieve Goal	Date Goal Achieved
Figure Skating Goal	**What I Need to Do to Achieve This Goal**	
What I Learned While Working Toward This Goal		

Date Goal Set	Target Date to Achieve Goal	Date Goal Achieved
Figure Skating Goal	**What I Need to Do to Achieve This Goal**	
What I Learned While Working Toward This Goal		

Figure Skating Goals

Date Goal Set	Target Date to Achieve Goal	Date Goal Achieved
Figure Skating Goal	**What I Need to Do to Achieve This Goal**	
What I Learned While Working Toward This Goal		

Date Goal Set	Target Date to Achieve Goal	Date Goal Achieved
Figure Skating Goal	**What I Need to Do to Achieve This Goal**	
What I Learned While Working Toward This Goal		

Date Goal Set	Target Date to Achieve Goal	Date Goal Achieved
Figure Skating Goal	**What I Need to Do to Achieve This Goal**	
What I Learned While Working Toward This Goal		

Figure Skating Goals

Date Goal Set	Target Date to Achieve Goal	Date Goal Achieved
Figure Skating Goal	**What I Need to Do to Achieve This Goal**	

What I Learned While Working Toward This Goal

Date Goal Set	Target Date to Achieve Goal	Date Goal Achieved
Figure Skating Goal	**What I Need to Do to Achieve This Goal**	

What I Learned While Working Toward This Goal

Date Goal Set	Target Date to Achieve Goal	Date Goal Achieved
Figure Skating Goal	**What I Need to Do to Achieve This Goal**	

What I Learned While Working Toward This Goal

Figure Skating Goals

Date Goal Set	Target Date to Achieve Goal	Date Goal Achieved
Figure Skating Goal	**What I Need to Do to Achieve This Goal**	
What I Learned While Working Toward This Goal		

Date Goal Set	Target Date to Achieve Goal	Date Goal Achieved
Figure Skating Goal	**What I Need to Do to Achieve This Goal**	
What I Learned While Working Toward This Goal		

Date Goal Set	Target Date to Achieve Goal	Date Goal Achieved
Figure Skating Goal	**What I Need to Do to Achieve This Goal**	
What I Learned While Working Toward This Goal		

Figure Skating Goals

Date Goal Set	Target Date to Achieve Goal	Date Goal Achieved
Figure Skating Goal	**What I Need to Do to Achieve This Goal**	
What I Learned While Working Toward This Goal		

Date Goal Set	Target Date to Achieve Goal	Date Goal Achieved
Figure Skating Goal	**What I Need to Do to Achieve This Goal**	
What I Learned While Working Toward This Goal		

Date Goal Set	Target Date to Achieve Goal	Date Goal Achieved
Figure Skating Goal	**What I Need to Do to Achieve This Goal**	
What I Learned While Working Toward This Goal		

Figure Skating Goals

Date Goal Set	Target Date to Achieve Goal	Date Goal Achieved
Figure Skating Goal	**What I Need to Do to Achieve This Goal**	
What I Learned While Working Toward This Goal		

Date Goal Set	Target Date to Achieve Goal	Date Goal Achieved
Figure Skating Goal	**What I Need to Do to Achieve This Goal**	
What I Learned While Working Toward This Goal		

Date Goal Set	Target Date to Achieve Goal	Date Goal Achieved
Figure Skating Goal	**What I Need to Do to Achieve This Goal**	
What I Learned While Working Toward This Goal		

Figure Skating Goals

Date Goal Set	Target Date to Achieve Goal	Date Goal Achieved
Figure Skating Goal	What I Need to Do to Achieve This Goal	
What I Learned While Working Toward This Goal		

Date Goal Set	Target Date to Achieve Goal	Date Goal Achieved
Figure Skating Goal	What I Need to Do to Achieve This Goal	
What I Learned While Working Toward This Goal		

Date Goal Set	Target Date to Achieve Goal	Date Goal Achieved
Figure Skating Goal	What I Need to Do to Achieve This Goal	
What I Learned While Working Toward This Goal		

Figure Skating Goals

Date Goal Set	Target Date to Achieve Goal	Date Goal Achieved
Figure Skating Goal	**What I Need to Do to Achieve This Goal**	
What I Learned While Working Toward This Goal		

Date Goal Set	Target Date to Achieve Goal	Date Goal Achieved
Figure Skating Goal	**What I Need to Do to Achieve This Goal**	
What I Learned While Working Toward This Goal		

Date Goal Set	Target Date to Achieve Goal	Date Goal Achieved
Figure Skating Goal	**What I Need to Do to Achieve This Goal**	
What I Learned While Working Toward This Goal		

Figure Skating Goals

Date Goal Set	Target Date to Achieve Goal	Date Goal Achieved
Figure Skating Goal	What I Need to Do to Achieve This Goal	
What I Learned While Working Toward This Goal		

Date Goal Set	Target Date to Achieve Goal	Date Goal Achieved
Figure Skating Goal	What I Need to Do to Achieve This Goal	
What I Learned While Working Toward This Goal		

Date Goal Set	Target Date to Achieve Goal	Date Goal Achieved
Figure Skating Goal	What I Need to Do to Achieve This Goal	
What I Learned While Working Toward This Goal		

Figure Skating Goals

Date Goal Set	Target Date to Achieve Goal	Date Goal Achieved
Figure Skating Goal	**What I Need to Do to Achieve This Goal**	
What I Learned While Working Toward This Goal		

Date Goal Set	Target Date to Achieve Goal	Date Goal Achieved
Figure Skating Goal	**What I Need to Do to Achieve This Goal**	
What I Learned While Working Toward This Goal		

Date Goal Set	Target Date to Achieve Goal	Date Goal Achieved
Figure Skating Goal	**What I Need to Do to Achieve This Goal**	
What I Learned While Working Toward This Goal		

Figure Skating Goals

Date Goal Set	Target Date to Achieve Goal	Date Goal Achieved
Figure Skating Goal	What I Need to Do to Achieve This Goal	

What I Learned While Working Toward This Goal

Date Goal Set	Target Date to Achieve Goal	Date Goal Achieved
Figure Skating Goal	What I Need to Do to Achieve This Goal	

What I Learned While Working Toward This Goal

Date Goal Set	Target Date to Achieve Goal	Date Goal Achieved
Figure Skating Goal	What I Need to Do to Achieve This Goal	

What I Learned While Working Toward This Goal

Figure Skating Goals

Date Goal Set	Target Date to Achieve Goal	Date Goal Achieved
Figure Skating Goal	**What I Need to Do to Achieve This Goal**	
What I Learned While Working Toward This Goal		

Date Goal Set	Target Date to Achieve Goal	Date Goal Achieved
Figure Skating Goal	**What I Need to Do to Achieve This Goal**	
What I Learned While Working Toward This Goal		

Date Goal Set	Target Date to Achieve Goal	Date Goal Achieved
Figure Skating Goal	**What I Need to Do to Achieve This Goal**	
What I Learned While Working Toward This Goal		

Figure Skating Goals

Date Goal Set	Target Date to Achieve Goal	Date Goal Achieved
Figure Skating Goal	**What I Need to Do to Achieve This Goal**	
What I Learned While Working Toward This Goal		

Date Goal Set	Target Date to Achieve Goal	Date Goal Achieved
Figure Skating Goal	**What I Need to Do to Achieve This Goal**	
What I Learned While Working Toward This Goal		

Date Goal Set	Target Date to Achieve Goal	Date Goal Achieved
Figure Skating Goal	**What I Need to Do to Achieve This Goal**	
What I Learned While Working Toward This Goal		

Figure Skating Goals

Date Goal Set	Target Date to Achieve Goal	Date Goal Achieved
Figure Skating Goal	What I Need to Do to Achieve This Goal	
What I Learned While Working Toward This Goal		

Date Goal Set	Target Date to Achieve Goal	Date Goal Achieved
Figure Skating Goal	What I Need to Do to Achieve This Goal	
What I Learned While Working Toward This Goal		

Date Goal Set	Target Date to Achieve Goal	Date Goal Achieved
Figure Skating Goal	What I Need to Do to Achieve This Goal	
What I Learned While Working Toward This Goal		

Freestyle Etiquette

Whenever you skate at a new rink, find the posted Freestyle Session Rules and read them. If the rink doesn't have them, you can use these as a guideline. Following these guidelines will make for a safer and more enjoyable skating experience.

1. **BE AWARE OF WHAT IS HAPPENING AROUND YOU** – always look for oncoming "traffic" before leaving the boards or center ice. Skating traffic usually moves counterclockwise around the ice. Look for oncoming skaters, particularly skaters in a Moves in the Field or dance pattern.
2. **GIVE THE PROPER RIGHT OF WAY** – Generally the Right of Way is granted to:
    a. Skaters executing a spin. They can't see you and they can't move out of your way. You must go around them.
    b. Skaters doing a program when their music is playing. They may be wearing a special color belt or sash. Try to give them room.
    c. In some rinks: Skaters in a lesson with their coach.
3. **PAY ATTENTION TO THE PATTERNS OF SKATERS** - Skaters move quickly and in seemingly unpredictable patterns. However, usually a skater will perform a jump or spin in the same place while they are practicing. Ice dancers generally move in a serpentine pattern around the edges of the ice. Learn to recognize the patterns of the skaters so you can anticipate where they will be and avoid collisions. You should also attempt to be predictable in your practice habits.
4. **SPINS IN THE MIDDLE, JUMPS IN THE ENDS** –spins should be done in the center of the ice, and jumps are performed in the corners or ends of the ice. This helps with predictability.
5. **HIGHER LEVEL SKATERS SHOULD LOOK OUT FOR LOWER LEVEL SKATERS** – a higher level skater can move more quickly out of the way than a lower level skater.
6. **ALWAYS LOOK BEHIND YOU WHEN SKATING BACKWARDS** – you must always keep your eye out for other skaters. If you can't be watching have your coach or a friend watch for you. Avoid skating backwards on the more crowded side of the rink (usually where the hockey boxes are).
7. **DO NOT PLAY YOUR MUSIC REPEATEDLY** –Make sure everyone has a chance to play their music.
8. **DON'T STAND TALKING IN THE CENTER OF THE ICE** – move to the boards when you are having a conversation that lasts more than a few seconds. Always keep moving or else move to the boards.
9. **BE NICE** – Rudeness, shouting, bullying, foul language, offensiveness, antagonizing, getting in other people's way on purpose, and other mean behavior will not be tolerated in any practice session or skating event.
10. **BE SUPPORTIVE OF ALL OTHER SKATERS** – Leave the judging to the competition judges. Jealousy and hate makes for a toxic environment that helps no one. Be happy for the accomplishments of your fellow skaters, and supportive when having problems. Everyone will benefit from a positive training environment.
11. **NO FOOD OR DRINK ON THE ICE** – a water bottle at the boards is permitted.
12. **KEEP TRACK OF YOUR BELONGINGS** – keep your own bags, water bottles, and jackets neatly together.

Skating Practice Notes

Skating Practice Notes

Practice Date	Place	Coach	Rating (1-10)
Skills Practiced	**Things to Remember**		

This Is What I Did Today to Work Toward My Skating Goals:

Today's Highlight

Practice Date	Place	Coach	Rating (1-10)
Skills Practiced	**Things to Remember**		

This Is What I Did Today to Work Toward My Skating Goals:

Today's Highlight

Skating Practice Notes

Practice Date	Place	Coach	Rating (1-10)
Skills Practiced	**Things to Remember**		

This Is What I Did Today to Work Toward My Skating Goals:

Today's Highlight

Practice Date	Place	Coach	Rating (1-10)
Skills Practiced	**Things to Remember**		

This Is What I Did Today to Work Toward My Skating Goals:

Today's Highlight

Skating Practice Notes

Practice Date	Place	Coach	Rating (1-10)
Skills Practiced	**Things to Remember**		

This Is What I Did Today to Work Toward My Skating Goals:

Today's Highlight

Practice Date	Place	Coach	Rating (1-10)
Skills Practiced	**Things to Remember**		

This Is What I Did Today to Work Toward My Skating Goals:

Today's Highlight

Skating Practice Notes

Practice Date	Place	Coach	Rating (1-10)
Skills Practiced	**Things to Remember**		
This Is What I Did Today to Work Toward My Skating Goals:			
Today's Highlight			

Practice Date	Place	Coach	Rating (1-10)
Skills Practiced	**Things to Remember**		
This Is What I Did Today to Work Toward My Skating Goals:			
Today's Highlight			

Skating Practice Notes

Practice Date	Place	Coach	Rating (1-10)
Skills Practiced	**Things to Remember**		

This Is What I Did Today to Work Toward My Skating Goals:

Today's Highlight

Practice Date	Place	Coach	Rating (1-10)
Skills Practiced	**Things to Remember**		

This Is What I Did Today to Work Toward My Skating Goals:

Today's Highlight

Skating Practice Notes

Practice Date	Place	Coach	Rating (1-10)
Skills Practiced	**Things to Remember**		

This Is What I Did Today to Work Toward My Skating Goals:

Today's Highlight

Practice Date	Place	Coach	Rating (1-10)
Skills Practiced	**Things to Remember**		

This Is What I Did Today to Work Toward My Skating Goals:

Today's Highlight

Skating Practice Notes

Practice Date	Place	Coach	Rating (1-10)
Skills Practiced	**Things to Remember**		

This Is What I Did Today to Work Toward My Skating Goals:

Today's Highlight

Practice Date	Place	Coach	Rating (1-10)
Skills Practiced	**Things to Remember**		

This Is What I Did Today to Work Toward My Skating Goals:

Today's Highlight

Skating Practice Notes

Practice Date	Place	Coach	Rating (1-10)
Skills Practiced	**Things to Remember**		

This Is What I Did Today to Work Toward My Skating Goals:

Today's Highlight

Practice Date	Place	Coach	Rating (1-10)
Skills Practiced	**Things to Remember**		

This Is What I Did Today to Work Toward My Skating Goals:

Today's Highlight

Skating Practice Notes

Practice Date	Place	Coach	Rating (1-10)

Skills Practiced	Things to Remember

This Is What I Did Today to Work Toward My Skating Goals:

Today's Highlight

Practice Date	Place	Coach	Rating (1-10)

Skills Practiced	Things to Remember

This Is What I Did Today to Work Toward My Skating Goals:

Today's Highlight

Skating Practice Notes

Practice Date	Place	Coach	Rating (1-10)
Skills Practiced	**Things to Remember**		

This Is What I Did Today to Work Toward My Skating Goals:

Today's Highlight

Practice Date	Place	Coach	Rating (1-10)
Skills Practiced	**Things to Remember**		

This Is What I Did Today to Work Toward My Skating Goals:

Today's Highlight

Skating Practice Notes

Practice Date	Place	Coach	Rating (1-10)
Skills Practiced	**Things to Remember**		

This Is What I Did Today to Work Toward My Skating Goals:

Today's Highlight

Practice Date	Place	Coach	Rating (1-10)
Skills Practiced	**Things to Remember**		

This Is What I Did Today to Work Toward My Skating Goals:

Today's Highlight

Skating Practice Notes

Practice Date	Place	Coach	Rating (1-10)
Skills Practiced	**Things to Remember**		

This Is What I Did Today to Work Toward My Skating Goals:

Today's Highlight

Practice Date	Place	Coach	Rating (1-10)
Skills Practiced	**Things to Remember**		

This Is What I Did Today to Work Toward My Skating Goals:

Today's Highlight

Skating Practice Notes

Practice Date	Place	Coach	Rating (1-10)
Skills Practiced	**Things to Remember**		

This Is What I Did Today to Work Toward My Skating Goals:

Today's Highlight

Practice Date	Place	Coach	Rating (1-10)
Skills Practiced	**Things to Remember**		

This Is What I Did Today to Work Toward My Skating Goals:

Today's Highlight

Skating Practice Notes

Practice Date	Place	Coach	Rating (1-10)
Skills Practiced	**Things to Remember**		

This Is What I Did Today to Work Toward My Skating Goals:

Today's Highlight

Practice Date	Place	Coach	Rating (1-10)
Skills Practiced	**Things to Remember**		

This Is What I Did Today to Work Toward My Skating Goals:

Today's Highlight

Skating Practice Notes

Practice Date	Place	Coach	Rating (1-10)

Skills Practiced	Things to Remember

This Is What I Did Today to Work Toward My Skating Goals:

Today's Highlight

Practice Date	Place	Coach	Rating (1-10)

Skills Practiced	Things to Remember

This Is What I Did Today to Work Toward My Skating Goals:

Today's Highlight

Skating Practice Notes

Practice Date	Place	Coach	Rating (1-10)
Skills Practiced	**Things to Remember**		

This Is What I Did Today to Work Toward My Skating Goals:

Today's Highlight

Practice Date	Place	Coach	Rating (1-10)
Skills Practiced	**Things to Remember**		

This Is What I Did Today to Work Toward My Skating Goals:

Today's Highlight

Skating Practice Notes

Practice Date	Place	Coach	Rating (1-10)
Skills Practiced	**Things to Remember**		

This Is What I Did Today to Work Toward My Skating Goals:

Today's Highlight

Practice Date	Place	Coach	Rating (1-10)
Skills Practiced	**Things to Remember**		

This Is What I Did Today to Work Toward My Skating Goals:

Today's Highlight

Skating Practice Notes

Practice Date	Place	Coach	Rating (1-10)
Skills Practiced	**Things to Remember**		

This Is What I Did Today to Work Toward My Skating Goals:

Today's Highlight

Practice Date	Place	Coach	Rating (1-10)
Skills Practiced	**Things to Remember**		

This Is What I Did Today to Work Toward My Skating Goals:

Today's Highlight

Skating Practice Notes

Practice Date	Place	Coach	Rating (1-10)

Skills Practiced	Things to Remember

This Is What I Did Today to Work Toward My Skating Goals:

Today's Highlight

Practice Date	Place	Coach	Rating (1-10)

Skills Practiced	Things to Remember

This Is What I Did Today to Work Toward My Skating Goals:

Today's Highlight

Skating Practice Notes

Practice Date	Place	Coach	Rating (1-10)
Skills Practiced	**Things to Remember**		

This Is What I Did Today to Work Toward My Skating Goals:

Today's Highlight

Practice Date	Place	Coach	Rating (1-10)
Skills Practiced	**Things to Remember**		

This Is What I Did Today to Work Toward My Skating Goals:

Today's Highlight

Skating Practice Notes

Practice Date	Place	Coach	Rating (1-10)
Skills Practiced	**Things to Remember**		

This Is What I Did Today to Work Toward My Skating Goals:

Today's Highlight

Practice Date	Place	Coach	Rating (1-10)
Skills Practiced	**Things to Remember**		

This Is What I Did Today to Work Toward My Skating Goals:

Today's Highlight

Skating Practice Notes

Practice Date	Place	Coach	Rating (1-10)
Skills Practiced	**Things to Remember**		

This Is What I Did Today to Work Toward My Skating Goals:

Today's Highlight

Practice Date	Place	Coach	Rating (1-10)
Skills Practiced	**Things to Remember**		

This Is What I Did Today to Work Toward My Skating Goals:

Today's Highlight

Skating Practice Notes

Practice Date	Place	Coach	Rating (1-10)
Skills Practiced	**Things to Remember**		
This Is What I Did Today to Work Toward My Skating Goals:			
Today's Highlight			

Practice Date	Place	Coach	Rating (1-10)
Skills Practiced	**Things to Remember**		
This Is What I Did Today to Work Toward My Skating Goals:			
Today's Highlight			

Skating Practice Notes

Practice Date	Place	Coach	Rating (1-10)
Skills Practiced	**Things to Remember**		

This Is What I Did Today to Work Toward My Skating Goals:

Today's Highlight

Practice Date	Place	Coach	Rating (1-10)
Skills Practiced	**Things to Remember**		

This Is What I Did Today to Work Toward My Skating Goals:

Today's Highlight

Skating Practice Notes

Practice Date	Place	Coach	Rating (1-10)
Skills Practiced	**Things to Remember**		

This Is What I Did Today to Work Toward My Skating Goals:

Today's Highlight

Practice Date	Place	Coach	Rating (1-10)
Skills Practiced	**Things to Remember**		

This Is What I Did Today to Work Toward My Skating Goals:

Today's Highlight

Skating Practice Notes

Practice Date	Place	Coach	Rating (1-10)

Skills Practiced	Things to Remember

This Is What I Did Today to Work Toward My Skating Goals:

Today's Highlight

Practice Date	Place	Coach	Rating (1-10)

Skills Practiced	Things to Remember

This Is What I Did Today to Work Toward My Skating Goals:

Today's Highlight

Skating Practice Notes

Practice Date	Place	Coach	Rating (1-10)
Skills Practiced	**Things to Remember**		

This Is What I Did Today to Work Toward My Skating Goals:

Today's Highlight

Practice Date	Place	Coach	Rating (1-10)
Skills Practiced	**Things to Remember**		

This Is What I Did Today to Work Toward My Skating Goals:

Today's Highlight

Skating Practice Notes

Practice Date	Place	Coach	Rating (1-10)
Skills Practiced	**Things to Remember**		

This Is What I Did Today to Work Toward My Skating Goals:

Today's Highlight

Practice Date	Place	Coach	Rating (1-10)
Skills Practiced	**Things to Remember**		

This Is What I Did Today to Work Toward My Skating Goals:

Today's Highlight

Skating Practice Notes

Practice Date	Place	Coach	Rating (1-10)

Skills Practiced	Things to Remember

This Is What I Did Today to Work Toward My Skating Goals:

Today's Highlight

Practice Date	Place	Coach	Rating (1-10)

Skills Practiced	Things to Remember

This Is What I Did Today to Work Toward My Skating Goals:

Today's Highlight

Skating Practice Notes

Practice Date	Place	Coach	Rating (1-10)
Skills Practiced	**Things to Remember**		

This Is What I Did Today to Work Toward My Skating Goals:

Today's Highlight

Practice Date	Place	Coach	Rating (1-10)
Skills Practiced	**Things to Remember**		

This Is What I Did Today to Work Toward My Skating Goals:

Today's Highlight

Skating Practice Notes

Practice Date	Place	Coach	Rating (1-10)

Skills Practiced	Things to Remember

This Is What I Did Today to Work Toward My Skating Goals:

Today's Highlight

Practice Date	Place	Coach	Rating (1-10)

Skills Practiced	Things to Remember

This Is What I Did Today to Work Toward My Skating Goals:

Today's Highlight

Skating Practice Notes

Practice Date	Place	Coach	Rating (1-10)
Skills Practiced	**Things to Remember**		

This Is What I Did Today to Work Toward My Skating Goals:

Today's Highlight

Practice Date	Place	Coach	Rating (1-10)
Skills Practiced	**Things to Remember**		

This Is What I Did Today to Work Toward My Skating Goals:

Today's Highlight

Skating Practice Notes

Practice Date	Place	Coach	Rating (1-10)

Skills Practiced	Things to Remember

This Is What I Did Today to Work Toward My Skating Goals:

Today's Highlight

Practice Date	Place	Coach	Rating (1-10)

Skills Practiced	Things to Remember

This Is What I Did Today to Work Toward My Skating Goals:

Today's Highlight

Skating Practice Notes

Practice Date	Place	Coach	Rating (1-10)
Skills Practiced	**Things to Remember**		

This Is What I Did Today to Work Toward My Skating Goals:

Today's Highlight

Practice Date	Place	Coach	Rating (1-10)
Skills Practiced	**Things to Remember**		

This Is What I Did Today to Work Toward My Skating Goals:

Today's Highlight

Skating Practice Notes

Practice Date	Place	Coach	Rating (1-10)
Skills Practiced	**Things to Remember**		

This Is What I Did Today to Work Toward My Skating Goals:

Today's Highlight

Practice Date	Place	Coach	Rating (1-10)
Skills Practiced	**Things to Remember**		

This Is What I Did Today to Work Toward My Skating Goals:

Today's Highlight

Skating Practice Notes

Practice Date	Place	Coach	Rating (1-10)
Skills Practiced	**Things to Remember**		

This Is What I Did Today to Work Toward My Skating Goals:

Today's Highlight

Practice Date	Place	Coach	Rating (1-10)
Skills Practiced	**Things to Remember**		

This Is What I Did Today to Work Toward My Skating Goals:

Today's Highlight

Skating Practice Notes

Practice Date	Place	Coach	Rating (1-10)
Skills Practiced	**Things to Remember**		

This Is What I Did Today to Work Toward My Skating Goals:

Today's Highlight

Practice Date	Place	Coach	Rating (1-10)
Skills Practiced	**Things to Remember**		

This Is What I Did Today to Work Toward My Skating Goals:

Today's Highlight

Skating Practice Notes

Practice Date	Place	Coach	Rating (1-10)
Skills Practiced	Things to Remember		

This Is What I Did Today to Work Toward My Skating Goals:

Today's Highlight

Practice Date	Place	Coach	Rating (1-10)
Skills Practiced	Things to Remember		

This Is What I Did Today to Work Toward My Skating Goals:

Today's Highlight

Skating Practice Notes

Practice Date	Place	Coach	Rating (1-10)
Skills Practiced	**Things to Remember**		

This Is What I Did Today to Work Toward My Skating Goals:

Today's Highlight

Practice Date	Place	Coach	Rating (1-10)
Skills Practiced	**Things to Remember**		

This Is What I Did Today to Work Toward My Skating Goals:

Today's Highlight

Skating Practice Notes

Practice Date	Place	Coach	Rating (1-10)
Skills Practiced	**Things to Remember**		

This Is What I Did Today to Work Toward My Skating Goals:

Today's Highlight

Practice Date	Place	Coach	Rating (1-10)
Skills Practiced	**Things to Remember**		

This Is What I Did Today to Work Toward My Skating Goals:

Today's Highlight

Skating Practice Notes

Practice Date	Place	Coach	Rating (1-10)
Skills Practiced	**Things to Remember**		

This Is What I Did Today to Work Toward My Skating Goals:

Today's Highlight

Practice Date	Place	Coach	Rating (1-10)
Skills Practiced	**Things to Remember**		

This Is What I Did Today to Work Toward My Skating Goals:

Today's Highlight

Skating Practice Notes

Practice Date	Place	Coach	Rating (1-10)
Skills Practiced	**Things to Remember**		

This Is What I Did Today to Work Toward My Skating Goals:

Today's Highlight

Practice Date	Place	Coach	Rating (1-10)
Skills Practiced	**Things to Remember**		

This Is What I Did Today to Work Toward My Skating Goals:

Today's Highlight

Skating Practice Notes

Practice Date	Place	Coach	Rating (1-10)

Skills Practiced	Things to Remember

This Is What I Did Today to Work Toward My Skating Goals:

Today's Highlight

Practice Date	Place	Coach	Rating (1-10)

Skills Practiced	Things to Remember

This Is What I Did Today to Work Toward My Skating Goals:

Today's Highlight

Skating Practice Notes

Practice Date	Place	Coach	Rating (1-10)
Skills Practiced	**Things to Remember**		

This Is What I Did Today to Work Toward My Skating Goals:

Today's Highlight

Practice Date	Place	Coach	Rating (1-10)
Skills Practiced	**Things to Remember**		

This Is What I Did Today to Work Toward My Skating Goals:

Today's Highlight

Skating Practice Notes

Practice Date	Place	Coach	Rating (1-10)

Skills Practiced	Things to Remember

This Is What I Did Today to Work Toward My Skating Goals:

Today's Highlight

Practice Date	Place	Coach	Rating (1-10)

Skills Practiced	Things to Remember

This Is What I Did Today to Work Toward My Skating Goals:

Today's Highlight

Skating Practice Notes

Practice Date	Place	Coach	Rating (1-10)
Skills Practiced	**Things to Remember**		

This Is What I Did Today to Work Toward My Skating Goals:

Today's Highlight

Practice Date	Place	Coach	Rating (1-10)
Skills Practiced	**Things to Remember**		

This Is What I Did Today to Work Toward My Skating Goals:

Today's Highlight

Skating Practice Notes

Practice Date	Place	Coach	Rating (1-10)
Skills Practiced	**Things to Remember**		

This Is What I Did Today to Work Toward My Skating Goals:

Today's Highlight

Practice Date	Place	Coach	Rating (1-10)
Skills Practiced	**Things to Remember**		

This Is What I Did Today to Work Toward My Skating Goals:

Today's Highlight

Skating Practice Notes

Practice Date	Place	Coach	Rating (1-10)
Skills Practiced	Things to Remember		

This Is What I Did Today to Work Toward My Skating Goals:

Today's Highlight

Practice Date	Place	Coach	Rating (1-10)
Skills Practiced	Things to Remember		

This Is What I Did Today to Work Toward My Skating Goals:

Today's Highlight

Skating Practice Notes

Practice Date	Place	Coach	Rating (1-10)
Skills Practiced	**Things to Remember**		

This Is What I Did Today to Work Toward My Skating Goals:

Today's Highlight

Practice Date	Place	Coach	Rating (1-10)
Skills Practiced	**Things to Remember**		

This Is What I Did Today to Work Toward My Skating Goals:

Today's Highlight

Skating Practice Notes

Practice Date	Place	Coach	Rating (1-10)
Skills Practiced	**Things to Remember**		

This Is What I Did Today to Work Toward My Skating Goals:

Today's Highlight

Practice Date	Place	Coach	Rating (1-10)
Skills Practiced	**Things to Remember**		

This Is What I Did Today to Work Toward My Skating Goals:

Today's Highlight

Skating Practice Notes

Practice Date	Place	Coach	Rating (1-10)
Skills Practiced	**Things to Remember**		

This Is What I Did Today to Work Toward My Skating Goals:

Today's Highlight

Practice Date	Place	Coach	Rating (1-10)
Skills Practiced	**Things to Remember**		

This Is What I Did Today to Work Toward My Skating Goals:

Today's Highlight

Skating Practice Notes

Practice Date	Place	Coach	Rating (1-10)
Skills Practiced	**Things to Remember**		

This Is What I Did Today to Work Toward My Skating Goals:

Today's Highlight

Practice Date	Place	Coach	Rating (1-10)
Skills Practiced	**Things to Remember**		

This Is What I Did Today to Work Toward My Skating Goals:

Today's Highlight

Skating Practice Notes

Practice Date	Place	Coach	Rating (1-10)
Skills Practiced	Things to Remember		
This Is What I Did Today to Work Toward My Skating Goals:			
Today's Highlight			

Practice Date	Place	Coach	Rating (1-10)
Skills Practiced	Things to Remember		
This Is What I Did Today to Work Toward My Skating Goals:			
Today's Highlight			

Skating Practice Notes

Practice Date	Place	Coach	Rating (1-10)
Skills Practiced	**Things to Remember**		

This Is What I Did Today to Work Toward My Skating Goals:

Today's Highlight

Practice Date	Place	Coach	Rating (1-10)
Skills Practiced	**Things to Remember**		

This Is What I Did Today to Work Toward My Skating Goals:

Today's Highlight

Skating Practice Notes

Practice Date	Place	Coach	Rating (1-10)
Skills Practiced	Things to Remember		

This Is What I Did Today to Work Toward My Skating Goals:

Today's Highlight

Practice Date	Place	Coach	Rating (1-10)
Skills Practiced	Things to Remember		

This Is What I Did Today to Work Toward My Skating Goals:

Today's Highlight

Skating Practice Notes

Practice Date	Place	Coach	Rating (1-10)

Skills Practiced	Things to Remember

This Is What I Did Today to Work Toward My Skating Goals:

Today's Highlight

Practice Date	Place	Coach	Rating (1-10)

Skills Practiced	Things to Remember

This Is What I Did Today to Work Toward My Skating Goals:

Today's Highlight

Skating Practice Notes

Practice Date	Place	Coach	Rating (1-10)

Skills Practiced	Things to Remember

This Is What I Did Today to Work Toward My Skating Goals:

Today's Highlight

Practice Date	Place	Coach	Rating (1-10)

Skills Practiced	Things to Remember

This Is What I Did Today to Work Toward My Skating Goals:

Today's Highlight

Skating Practice Notes

Practice Date	Place	Coach	Rating (1-10)
Skills Practiced	**Things to Remember**		

This Is What I Did Today to Work Toward My Skating Goals:

Today's Highlight

Practice Date	Place	Coach	Rating (1-10)
Skills Practiced	**Things to Remember**		

This Is What I Did Today to Work Toward My Skating Goals:

Today's Highlight

Skating Practice Notes

Practice Date	Place	Coach	Rating (1-10)
Skills Practiced	**Things to Remember**		

This Is What I Did Today to Work Toward My Skating Goals:

Today's Highlight

Practice Date	Place	Coach	Rating (1-10)
Skills Practiced	**Things to Remember**		

This Is What I Did Today to Work Toward My Skating Goals:

Today's Highlight

Skating Practice Notes

Practice Date	Place	Coach	Rating (1-10)
Skills Practiced	**Things to Remember**		

This Is What I Did Today to Work Toward My Skating Goals:

Today's Highlight

Practice Date	Place	Coach	Rating (1-10)
Skills Practiced	**Things to Remember**		

This Is What I Did Today to Work Toward My Skating Goals:

Today's Highlight

Skating Practice Notes

Practice Date	Place	Coach	Rating (1-10)
Skills Practiced	Things to Remember		

This Is What I Did Today to Work Toward My Skating Goals:

Today's Highlight

Practice Date	Place	Coach	Rating (1-10)
Skills Practiced	Things to Remember		

This Is What I Did Today to Work Toward My Skating Goals:

Today's Highlight

Skating Practice Notes

Practice Date	Place	Coach	Rating (1-10)
Skills Practiced	**Things to Remember**		

This Is What I Did Today to Work Toward My Skating Goals:

Today's Highlight

Practice Date	Place	Coach	Rating (1-10)
Skills Practiced	**Things to Remember**		

This Is What I Did Today to Work Toward My Skating Goals:

Today's Highlight

Skating Practice Notes

Practice Date	Place	Coach	Rating (1-10)
Skills Practiced	**Things to Remember**		

This Is What I Did Today to Work Toward My Skating Goals:

Today's Highlight

Practice Date	Place	Coach	Rating (1-10)
Skills Practiced	**Things to Remember**		

This Is What I Did Today to Work Toward My Skating Goals:

Today's Highlight

Skating Practice Notes

Practice Date	Place	Coach	Rating (1-10)
Skills Practiced	**Things to Remember**		

This Is What I Did Today to Work Toward My Skating Goals:

Today's Highlight

Practice Date	Place	Coach	Rating (1-10)
Skills Practiced	**Things to Remember**		

This Is What I Did Today to Work Toward My Skating Goals:

Today's Highlight

Skating Practice Notes

Practice Date	Place	Coach	Rating (1-10)
Skills Practiced	**Things to Remember**		

This Is What I Did Today to Work Toward My Skating Goals:

Today's Highlight

Practice Date	Place	Coach	Rating (1-10)
Skills Practiced	**Things to Remember**		

This Is What I Did Today to Work Toward My Skating Goals:

Today's Highlight

Skating Practice Notes

Practice Date	Place	Coach	Rating (1-10)

Skills Practiced	Things to Remember

This Is What I Did Today to Work Toward My Skating Goals:

Today's Highlight

Practice Date	Place	Coach	Rating (1-10)

Skills Practiced	Things to Remember

This Is What I Did Today to Work Toward My Skating Goals:

Today's Highlight

Skating Practice Notes

Practice Date	Place	Coach	Rating (1-10)
Skills Practiced	**Things to Remember**		

This Is What I Did Today to Work Toward My Skating Goals:

Today's Highlight

Practice Date	Place	Coach	Rating (1-10)
Skills Practiced	**Things to Remember**		

This Is What I Did Today to Work Toward My Skating Goals:

Today's Highlight

Skating Practice Notes

Practice Date	Place	Coach	Rating (1-10)
Skills Practiced	**Things to Remember**		

This Is What I Did Today to Work Toward My Skating Goals:

Today's Highlight

Practice Date	Place	Coach	Rating (1-10)
Skills Practiced	**Things to Remember**		

This Is What I Did Today to Work Toward My Skating Goals:

Today's Highlight

Skating Practice Notes

Practice Date	Place	Coach	Rating (1-10)
Skills Practiced	**Things to Remember**		

This Is What I Did Today to Work Toward My Skating Goals:

Today's Highlight

Practice Date	Place	Coach	Rating (1-10)
Skills Practiced	**Things to Remember**		

This Is What I Did Today to Work Toward My Skating Goals:

Today's Highlight

Skating Practice Notes

Practice Date	Place	Coach	Rating (1-10)
Skills Practiced	**Things to Remember**		

This Is What I Did Today to Work Toward My Skating Goals:

Today's Highlight

Practice Date	Place	Coach	Rating (1-10)
Skills Practiced	**Things to Remember**		

This Is What I Did Today to Work Toward My Skating Goals:

Today's Highlight

Skating Practice Notes

Practice Date	Place	Coach	Rating (1-10)

Skills Practiced	Things to Remember

This Is What I Did Today to Work Toward My Skating Goals:

Today's Highlight

Practice Date	Place	Coach	Rating (1-10)

Skills Practiced	Things to Remember

This Is What I Did Today to Work Toward My Skating Goals:

Today's Highlight

Skating Practice Notes

Practice Date	Place	Coach	Rating (1-10)
Skills Practiced	**Things to Remember**		

This Is What I Did Today to Work Toward My Skating Goals:

Today's Highlight

Practice Date	Place	Coach	Rating (1-10)
Skills Practiced	**Things to Remember**		

This Is What I Did Today to Work Toward My Skating Goals:

Today's Highlight

Skating Practice Notes

Practice Date	Place	Coach	Rating (1-10)

Skills Practiced	Things to Remember

This Is What I Did Today to Work Toward My Skating Goals:

Today's Highlight

Practice Date	Place	Coach	Rating (1-10)

Skills Practiced	Things to Remember

This Is What I Did Today to Work Toward My Skating Goals:

Today's Highlight

Skating Practice Notes

Practice Date	Place	Coach	Rating (1-10)
Skills Practiced	**Things to Remember**		

This Is What I Did Today to Work Toward My Skating Goals:

Today's Highlight

Practice Date	Place	Coach	Rating (1-10)
Skills Practiced	**Things to Remember**		

This Is What I Did Today to Work Toward My Skating Goals:

Today's Highlight

Skating Practice Notes

Practice Date	Place	Coach	Rating (1-10)

Skills Practiced	Things to Remember

This Is What I Did Today to Work Toward My Skating Goals:

Today's Highlight

Practice Date	Place	Coach	Rating (1-10)

Skills Practiced	Things to Remember

This Is What I Did Today to Work Toward My Skating Goals:

Today's Highlight

Skating Practice Notes

Practice Date	Place	Coach	Rating (1-10)
Skills Practiced	**Things to Remember**		

This Is What I Did Today to Work Toward My Skating Goals:

Today's Highlight

Practice Date	Place	Coach	Rating (1-10)
Skills Practiced	**Things to Remember**		

This Is What I Did Today to Work Toward My Skating Goals:

Today's Highlight

Skating Practice Notes

Practice Date	Place	Coach	Rating (1-10)
Skills Practiced	**Things to Remember**		

This Is What I Did Today to Work Toward My Skating Goals:

Today's Highlight

Practice Date	Place	Coach	Rating (1-10)
Skills Practiced	**Things to Remember**		

This Is What I Did Today to Work Toward My Skating Goals:

Today's Highlight

Skating Practice Notes

Practice Date	Place	Coach	Rating (1-10)

Skills Practiced	Things to Remember

This Is What I Did Today to Work Toward My Skating Goals:

Today's Highlight

Practice Date	Place	Coach	Rating (1-10)

Skills Practiced	Things to Remember

This Is What I Did Today to Work Toward My Skating Goals:

Today's Highlight

Skating Practice Notes

Practice Date	Place	Coach	Rating (1-10)
Skills Practiced	**Things to Remember**		

This Is What I Did Today to Work Toward My Skating Goals:

Today's Highlight

Practice Date	Place	Coach	Rating (1-10)
Skills Practiced	**Things to Remember**		

This Is What I Did Today to Work Toward My Skating Goals:

Today's Highlight

Skating Practice Notes

Practice Date	Place	Coach	Rating (1-10)
Skills Practiced	**Things to Remember**		

This Is What I Did Today to Work Toward My Skating Goals:

Today's Highlight

Practice Date	Place	Coach	Rating (1-10)
Skills Practiced	**Things to Remember**		

This Is What I Did Today to Work Toward My Skating Goals:

Today's Highlight

Testing Records

Testing Records

Date of Test	Test Name	Rink Name
Skills/Elements on This Test		**Score/Pass/Retry**
What I Learned While Working On This Test		**Total Score**

Date of Test	Test Name	Rink Name
Skills/Elements on This Test		**Score/Pass/Retry**
What I Learned While Working On This Test		**Total Score**

Testing Records

Date of Test	Test Name	Rink Name
Skills/Elements on This Test		**Score/Pass/Retry**
What I Learned While Working On This Test		**Total Score**

Date of Test	Test Name	Rink Name
Skills/Elements on This Test		**Score/Pass/Retry**
What I Learned While Working On This Test		**Total Score**

Testing Records

Date of Test	Test Name	Rink Name
Skills/Elements on This Test		Score/Pass/Retry
What I Learned While Working On This Test		Total Score

Date of Test	Test Name	Rink Name
Skills/Elements on This Test		Score/Pass/Retry
What I Learned While Working On This Test		Total Score

Testing Records

Date of Test	Test Name	Rink Name
Skills/Elements on This Test		Score/Pass/Retry
What I Learned While Working On This Test		Total Score

Date of Test	Test Name	Rink Name
Skills/Elements on This Test		Score/Pass/Retry
What I Learned While Working On This Test		Total Score

Testing Records

Date of Test	Test Name	Rink Name
Skills/Elements on This Test		**Score/Pass/Retry**
What I Learned While Working On This Test		**Total Score**

Date of Test	Test Name	Rink Name
Skills/Elements on This Test		**Score/Pass/Retry**
What I Learned While Working On This Test		**Total Score**

Testing Records

Date of Test	Test Name	Rink Name
Skills/Elements on This Test		**Score/Pass/Retry**
What I Learned While Working On This Test		**Total Score**

Date of Test	Test Name	Rink Name
Skills/Elements on This Test		**Score/Pass/Retry**
What I Learned While Working On This Test		**Total Score**

Testing Records

Date of Test	Test Name	Rink Name
Skills/Elements on This Test		**Score/Pass/Retry**
What I Learned While Working On This Test		**Total Score**

Date of Test	Test Name	Rink Name
Skills/Elements on This Test		**Score/Pass/Retry**
What I Learned While Working On This Test		**Total Score**

Testing Records

Date of Test	Test Name	Rink Name
Skills/Elements on This Test		**Score/Pass/Retry**
What I Learned While Working On This Test		**Total Score**

Date of Test	Test Name	Rink Name
Skills/Elements on This Test		**Score/Pass/Retry**
What I Learned While Working On This Test		**Total Score**

Testing Records

Date of Test	Test Name	Rink Name
Skills/Elements on This Test		**Score/Pass/Retry**
What I Learned While Working On This Test		**Total Score**

Date of Test	Test Name	Rink Name
Skills/Elements on This Test		**Score/Pass/Retry**
What I Learned While Working On This Test		**Total Score**

Testing Records

Date of Test	Test Name	Rink Name
Skills/Elements on This Test		Score/Pass/Retry
What I Learned While Working On This Test		Total Score

Date of Test	Test Name	Rink Name
Skills/Elements on This Test		Score/Pass/Retry
What I Learned While Working On This Test		Total Score

Competitions

Competitions

Competition Name	Date	Rink/Club Name
Event Name	Music	Program Length

Program Content

Placement (out of #)	Medal	Qualified for:
IJS: Technical Element Score:	Program Component Score:	Total Score:

Highlights of this Event:

Competition Name	Date	Rink/Club Name
Event Name	Music	Program Length

Program Content

Place (out of #)	Medal	Qualified for:
IJS: Technical Element Score:	Program Component Score:	Total Score:

Highlights of this Event:

Competitions

Competition Name	Date	Rink/Club Name
Event Name	Music	Program Length
Program Content		
Placement (out of #)	Medal	Qualified for:
IJS: Technical Element Score:	Program Component Score:	Total Score:
Highlights of this Event:		

Competition Name	Date	Rink/Club Name
Event Name	Music	Program Length
Program Content		
Place (out of #)	Medal	Qualified for:
IJS: Technical Element Score:	Program Component Score:	Total Score:
Highlights of this Event:		

Competitions

Competition Name	Date	Rink/Club Name
Event Name	Music	Program Length

Program Content

Placement (out of #)	Medal	Qualified for:
IJS: Technical Element Score:	Program Component Score:	Total Score:

Highlights of this Event:

Competition Name	Date	Rink/Club Name
Event Name	Music	Program Length

Program Content

Place (out of #)	Medal	Qualified for:
IJS: Technical Element Score:	Program Component Score:	Total Score:

Highlights of this Event:

Competitions

Competition Name	Date	Rink/Club Name
Event Name	Music	Program Length

Program Content

Placement (out of #)	Medal	Qualified for:
IJS: Technical Element Score:	Program Component Score:	Total Score:

Highlights of this Event:

Competition Name	Date	Rink/Club Name
Event Name	Music	Program Length

Program Content

Place (out of #)	Medal	Qualified for:
IJS: Technical Element Score:	Program Component Score:	Total Score:

Highlights of this Event:

Competitions

Competition Name	Date	Rink/Club Name
Event Name	**Music**	**Program Length**

Program Content

Placement (out of #)	Medal	Qualified for:
IJS: Technical Element Score:	Program Component Score:	Total Score:

Highlights of this Event:

Competition Name	Date	Rink/Club Name
Event Name	**Music**	**Program Length**

Program Content

Place (out of #)	Medal	Qualified for:
IJS: Technical Element Score:	Program Component Score:	Total Score:

Highlights of this Event:

Competitions

Competition Name	Date	Rink/Club Name
Event Name	Music	Program Length

Program Content

Placement (out of #)	Medal	Qualified for:
IJS: Technical Element Score:	Program Component Score:	Total Score:

Highlights of this Event:

Competition Name	Date	Rink/Club Name
Event Name	Music	Program Length

Program Content

Place (out of #)	Medal	Qualified for:
IJS: Technical Element Score:	Program Component Score:	Total Score:

Highlights of this Event:

Competitions

Competition Name	Date	Rink/Club Name
Event Name	Music	Program Length

Program Content

Placement (out of #)	Medal	Qualified for:
IJS: Technical Element Score:	Program Component Score:	Total Score:

Highlights of this Event:

Competition Name	Date	Rink/Club Name
Event Name	Music	Program Length

Program Content

Place (out of #)	Medal	Qualified for:
IJS: Technical Element Score:	Program Component Score:	Total Score:

Highlights of this Event:

Competitions

Competition Name	Date	Rink/Club Name
Event Name	Music	Program Length

Program Content

Placement (out of #)	Medal	Qualified for:
IJS: Technical Element Score:	Program Component Score:	Total Score:

Highlights of this Event:

Competition Name	Date	Rink/Club Name
Event Name	Music	Program Length

Program Content

Place (out of #)	Medal	Qualified for:
IJS: Technical Element Score:	Program Component Score:	Total Score:

Highlights of this Event:

Competitions

Competition Name	Date	Rink/Club Name
Event Name	Music	Program Length

Program Content		

Placement (out of #)	Medal	Qualified for:
IJS: Technical Element Score:	Program Component Score:	Total Score:

Highlights of this Event:		

Competition Name	Date	Rink/Club Name
Event Name	Music	Program Length

Program Content		

Place (out of #)	Medal	Qualified for:
IJS: Technical Element Score:	Program Component Score:	Total Score:

Highlights of this Event:		

Competitions

Competition Name	Date	Rink/Club Name
Event Name	Music	Program Length

Program Content

Placement (out of #)	Medal	Qualified for:
IJS: Technical Element Score:	Program Component Score:	Total Score:

Highlights of this Event:

Competition Name	Date	Rink/Club Name
Event Name	Music	Program Length

Program Content

Place (out of #)	Medal	Qualified for:
IJS: Technical Element Score:	Program Component Score:	Total Score:

Highlights of this Event:

Competitions

Competition Name	Date	Rink/Club Name
Event Name	Music	Program Length

Program Content

Placement (out of #)	Medal	Qualified for:
IJS: Technical Element Score:	Program Component Score:	Total Score:

Highlights of this Event:

Competition Name	Date	Rink/Club Name
Event Name	Music	Program Length

Program Content

Place (out of #)	Medal	Qualified for:
IJS: Technical Element Score:	Program Component Score:	Total Score:

Highlights of this Event:

Competitions

Competition Name	Date	Rink/Club Name
Event Name	Music	Program Length
Program Content		
Placement (out of #)	Medal	Qualified for:
IJS: Technical Element Score:	Program Component Score:	Total Score:
Highlights of this Event:		

Competition Name	Date	Rink/Club Name
Event Name	Music	Program Length
Program Content		
Place (out of #)	Medal	Qualified for:
IJS: Technical Element Score:	Program Component Score:	Total Score:
Highlights of this Event:		

Competitions

Competition Name	Date	Rink/Club Name
Event Name	Music	Program Length

Program Content

Placement (out of #)	Medal	Qualified for:
IJS: Technical Element Score:	Program Component Score:	Total Score:

Highlights of this Event:

Competition Name	Date	Rink/Club Name
Event Name	Music	Program Length

Program Content

Place (out of #)	Medal	Qualified for:
IJS: Technical Element Score:	Program Component Score:	Total Score:

Highlights of this Event:

Competitions

Competition Name	Date	Rink/Club Name

Event Name	Music	Program Length

Program Content

Placement (out of #)	Medal	Qualified for:
IJS: Technical Element Score:	Program Component Score:	Total Score:

Highlights of this Event:

Competition Name	Date	Rink/Club Name

Event Name	Music	Program Length

Program Content

Place (out of #)	Medal	Qualified for:
IJS: Technical Element Score:	Program Component Score:	Total Score:

Highlights of this Event:

Competitions

Competition Name	Date	Rink/Club Name
Event Name	Music	Program Length

Program Content

Placement (out of #)	Medal	Qualified for:
IJS: Technical Element Score:	Program Component Score:	Total Score:

Highlights of this Event:

Competition Name	Date	Rink/Club Name
Event Name	Music	Program Length

Program Content

Place (out of #)	Medal	Qualified for:
IJS: Technical Element Score:	Program Component Score:	Total Score:

Highlights of this Event:

Competitions

Competition Name	Date	Rink/Club Name
Event Name	Music	Program Length

Program Content

Placement (out of #)	Medal	Qualified for:
IJS: Technical Element Score:	Program Component Score:	Total Score:

Highlights of this Event:

Competition Name	Date	Rink/Club Name
Event Name	Music	Program Length

Program Content

Place (out of #)	Medal	Qualified for:
IJS: Technical Element Score:	Program Component Score:	Total Score:

Highlights of this Event:

Competitions

Competition Name	Date	Rink/Club Name
Event Name	Music	Program Length

Program Content

Placement (out of #)	Medal	Qualified for:
IJS: Technical Element Score:	Program Component Score:	Total Score:

Highlights of this Event:

Competition Name	Date	Rink/Club Name
Event Name	Music	Program Length

Program Content

Place (out of #)	Medal	Qualified for:
IJS: Technical Element Score:	Program Component Score:	Total Score:

Highlights of this Event:

Competitions

Competition Name	Date	Rink/Club Name
Event Name	Music	Program Length

Program Content

Placement (out of #)	Medal	Qualified for:
IJS: Technical Element Score:	Program Component Score:	Total Score:

Highlights of this Event:

Competition Name	Date	Rink/Club Name
Event Name	Music	Program Length

Program Content

Place (out of #)	Medal	Qualified for:
IJS: Technical Element Score:	Program Component Score:	Total Score:

Highlights of this Event:

Competitions

Competition Name	Date	Rink/Club Name
Event Name	Music	Program Length

Program Content

Placement (out of #)	Medal	Qualified for:
IJS: Technical Element Score:	Program Component Score:	Total Score:

Highlights of this Event:

Competition Name	Date	Rink/Club Name
Event Name	Music	Program Length

Program Content

Place (out of #)	Medal	Qualified for:
IJS: Technical Element Score:	Program Component Score:	Total Score:

Highlights of this Event:

Competitions

Competition Name	Date	Rink/Club Name
Event Name	Music	Program Length

Program Content

Placement (out of #)	Medal	Qualified for:
IJS: Technical Element Score:	Program Component Score:	Total Score:

Highlights of this Event:

Competition Name	Date	Rink/Club Name
Event Name	Music	Program Length

Program Content

Place (out of #)	Medal	Qualified for:
IJS: Technical Element Score:	Program Component Score:	Total Score:

Highlights of this Event:

Made in the USA
Middletown, DE
10 April 2019